PINNY'S
DAY
AT
PLAY SCHOOL

Text by JANE BELK MONCURE

Photographs by MORRIS H. JAFFE

LOTHROP, LEE AND SHEPARD CO., INC.

NEW YORK

The Author, Photographer,
and Publishers
express their thanks
to
The First Presbyterian Church
in The City of New York
for their cooperation
in photographing the children
in their nursery school

This is PINNY
She goes to school.

"Here I am,"
says Pinny to her teacher.

"I brought a piece of bread
for the mouse to eat."

"Eat your breakfast, mouse."

Pinny likes to fingerpaint.
"I'll paint the table top
all red."

"My hands are all red, too."

"I'll paint a picture
with a brush."

"When it's dry,
I'll take it home
to Mommy."

"Now I'll be a mommy
and wash the dishes."

"I'm the Daddy,"
says Haysie.
"I'm sick."

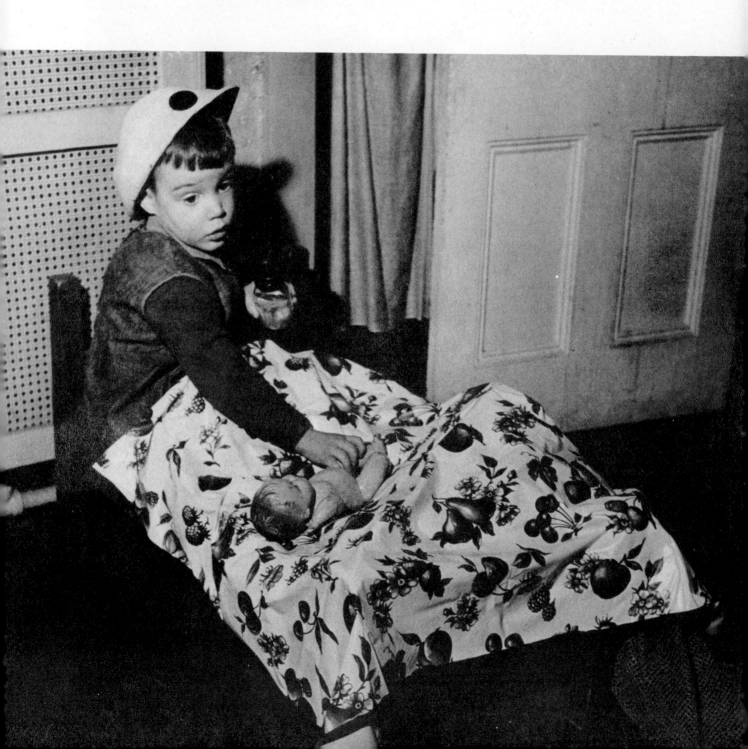

"Hello, doctor,
Haysie is sick.
Tell me what to do
to make him well."

The doctor says to make some soup,

and Pinny cooks it on the stove.

"Eat your soup, Haysie,
   and you will feel better."
Haysie eats his soup.
"I'm all well now," he says.

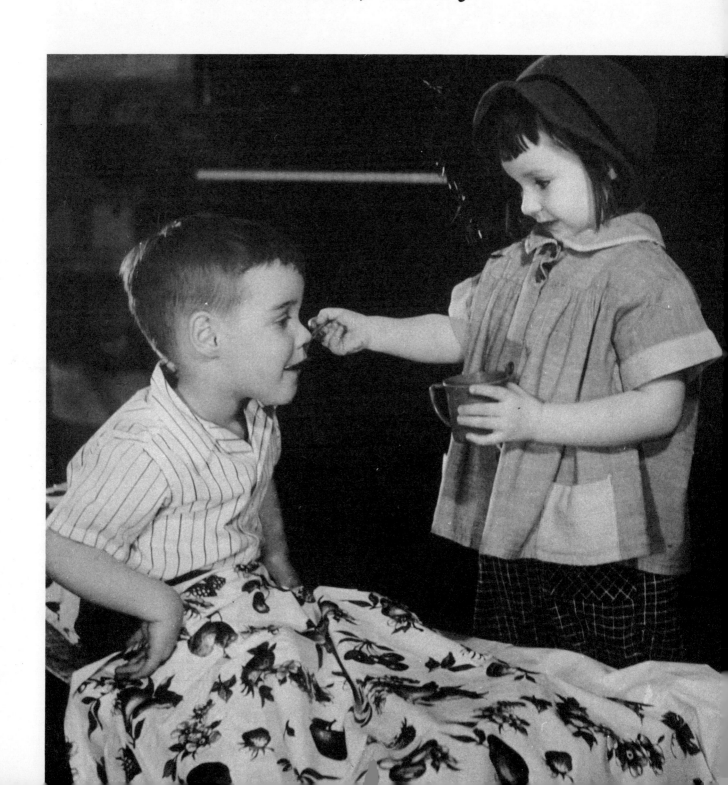

"Let's build a house for my bear, Pooh,"
says Pinny.

"I'll build a train station
near my house.
But where is the train?
Find it for me, Haysie."

"I want that train!"
Pinny says.
"No! it's mine!"
Haysie tells her.

"You took my train!"

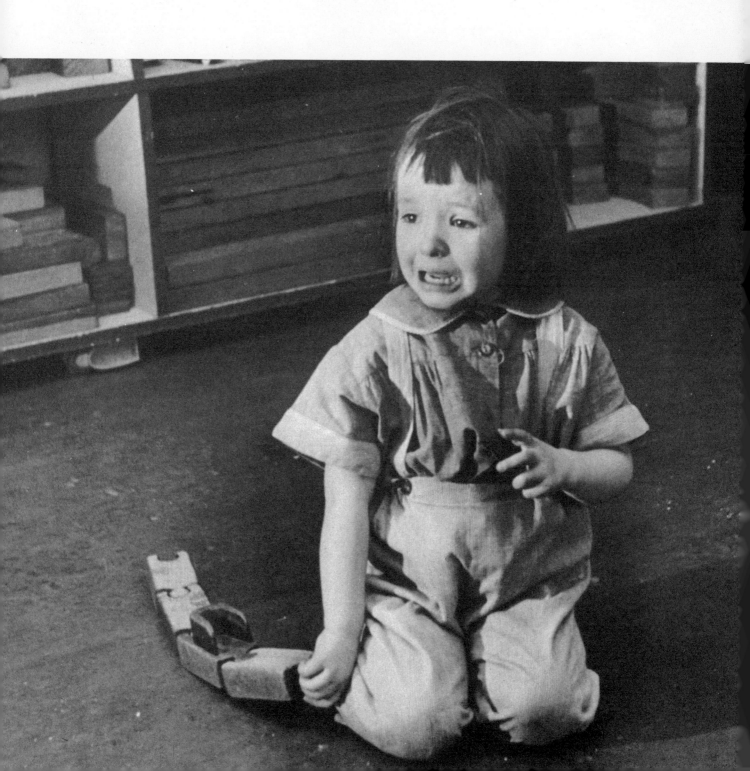

"We can have two trains, Pinny.
You have a train
and I have a train."

"Clean up time!"
 the teacher calls.
"Let's put the blocks away
 and I will tell you a story."

"This little girl
took an airplane ride.
She flew way up high."

"I can fly too."

Now it's time
to go out on
the play ground

"I have to
wiggle my foot
and pull hard,"
Pinny says,
putting on
her snowsuit.

She is the first one ready to go out.

Pinny reads a book

while she waits
for the other children.

Pinny likes to play outdoors.
"I'm driving my bus," says Pinny.
"Honk! Honk! Here we come!"

"This is a fire engine now.
Let's get the ladder."

"This is our bunny. He won't
eat his carrot, fat old bunny."

"I want to sing a song
  for Pooh," Pinny says.
"It's his birthday."

"Let's have a party! I'll make a cake."

"I'll light the candles."

"Happy birthday, Pooh!
You're two years old."

"Blow out the candles"

"Eat your cake. Isn't it good?"

"Let's blow the candles out again,"
says Laura.
"I like birthday parties best of all."

"Now it's time to go home, but

I'll be back again tomorrow!"